a better lifestyle for people in need of psychotherapeutic interventions. Let's not close the door of hope for those who need and seek assistance by hypnotherapeutic means!

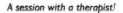

A session with a therapist!

Q. What is hypnotherapy?

A. Very simply, it's therapy conducted in a trance or hypnotic *state* of mind. Remember, whether it can be regarded as a state of mind is a contentious issue amongst academics, and should not really concern us if we are interested in *outcomes* and *results* of using such procedures. Believe it or not, any form of *effective* communication can be regarded as hypnotic! In hypnotherapy itself, a greater emphasis is placed upon inducing a trance state in you, with the use of suggestions to enhance potential and effect a desired change within you.

Interestingly, a greater use of hypnotherapeutic techniques are being employed by the medical professions. For example, in the treatment of irritable bowel syndrome (IBS), which does appear to have a psychosomatic component to the condition.

Q. What does the therapist actually do in the therapy sessions? What's their rôle?

A. Generally, the therapist will use his or her own voice in providing suitable suggestions and ideas, with or without the aid of an external physical device, to allow the client to experience a unique *state of altered awareness*. Remember that the time and the depth of this experience will vary from person to person, and with the time of day. As a result of this process, you will feel more relaxed, both mentally and physically, and just a nice, comfortable feeling of well-being will pervade within yourself.

As you may know, you will not always need a therapist to guide you through into this state of mind. You can actually do it all by yourself, provided you possess the required mental discipline that is expected of you. Briefly, you can guide yourself into your own self-induced relaxation, and the unique state of calm and receptiveness, by pretending to be the therapist and giving yourself autosuggestions of relaxation etc., consequently entering an autohypnotic state – this will be discussed a little later.

Importantly, the personal help and advice from a qualified therapist can assist you to achieve a much higher personal awareness and understanding of the processes involved; in addition to any friendly advice that might be provided to deal with your own personal situation or predicament.

Q. Explain to me what is meant by 'clinical hypnosis'?

A. I have indirectly touched on this question in my earlier answers. It means different things to different people depending on the particular philosophical standpoint a person follows or is influenced by – and I assure you there are many!

To put it briefly, it's the skilful use of words as an effective means of communication and the use of various techniques to elicit certain desired personal and therapeutic outcomes. It's the process of using the untapped potential within oneself to create a mental and physical change. Clinically, it has been used increasingly within the medical profession for various treatments and the relief of psychosomatic symptoms which have failed to respond to medication alone. It's a very natural and safe process, allowing your inner resources to adapt, change and evolve, and so creating transformation at both a mind and body level. *Reassociation* and *reorganisation* of thought patterns is facilitated in this hypnotic experience.

Q. I have heard people talking about the conscious and unconscious mind. What's meant by these terms?

A. These two terms are frequently used by hypnotherapists or clinicians using hypnosis as a form of treatment. There's no real advantage of using terms if they're not understood by the patients because they, the patients/clients, will not be able to make the required mental associations that is required of them. It's a little like conducting the whole therapy session in a foreign language and not knowing what's being spoken!

The *conscious mind* is often broadly referred to as the critical and the analytical capacity of the mind. The part that's involved in decision-making and so providing a logical dimension to your thinking process. In fact, from an academic perspective, the brain can be regarded as a very fluid structure, and the compartmentalisation of brain functions into rigid domains is debatable. Coming back to the hypnotherapeutic process, the therapist is putting you back in touch with your intuitive part of the inner mind – the so-called *unconscious mind*. Activating this aspect of your mind enables the bypassing, to a greater extent, of the critical faculty of the conscious mind. It may be worth noting that many therapists will

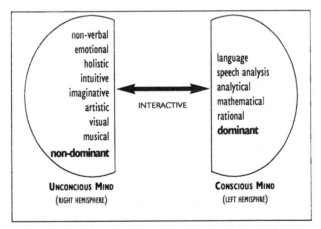

non-verbal
emotional
holistic
intuitive
imaginative
artistic
visual
musical
non-dominant

INTERACTIVE

language
speech analysis
analytical
mathematical
rational
dominant

UNCONCIOUS MIND
(RIGHT HEMISPHERE)

CONSCIOUS MIND
(LEFT HEMISPHRE)

Figure 1: The different functions attributed to the right and left brain hemispheres for a right-handed person (greatly simplified). There is a considerable overlap of functions between the hemispheres as depicted by the double arrow.

use the words unconscious and subconscious interchangeably to mean the same thing – so you needn't get confused if they do so during a therapy session!

So, basically, hypnosis work is generally centred on the unconscious mind, with the use of suggestions and the various types of imagery. By initiating a subtle change at an unconscious level in the way you think and rationalise things, you can effectively begin to change the way you feel and behave under various situations and circumstances. In fact, imagery, as it is often said, is the way our unconscious mind communicates and perceives. Usually, you first picture something, and then attach words to it as a part of a natural descriptive process, and so on.

Q. Are there any contra-indications for the use of self-hypnosis that I should be aware of?

A. There are a few things you should keep in mind when practising self-hypnosis. The first is that you should not be driving or operating any machinery because of the altered state of mind you will enter. Secondly, you should use self-hypnosis with caution if you suffer from epilepsy, although its use is not specifically contra-indicated in this condition. Initially, it may be wise for you to permit the clinical hypnotherapist to guide you through a self-hypnosis session(s), so that you can appreciate certain general guidelines. In fact, hypnosis has been used as an adjunct therapy to standard medication to treat some forms of epileptic seizures with some success – but only in the hands of a trained clinician.

Q. So, are you saying that hypnosis is not dangerous in any way?

A. No, I'm not! What I am saying, and the thing that everyone should understand, is that hypnosis by itself is not dangerous at all. It's only a therapeutic tool. If used within certain guidelines by a qualified therapist, then there's no problem at all.

The giving of inappropriate advice, whether in the state of hypnosis or not, is really the same thing and it is up to you to follow it or not. Don't forget that nobody can force an idea upon anyone against their will!

Let me also give you an example to explain my understanding of the matter. A kitchen knife by itself is a harmless utensil, but when put to inappropriate use, for example, for causing grievous bodily harm, then we have a problem. Similarly, the pen with which you write is a very important instrument of communication but can also be used as a crude weapon to produce, say, a puncture wound. I hope you understand the point I am trying to make. Hypnosis *by itself* is not dangerous.

Q. Does relaxation play an important rôle in therapy, for example, in the treatment of anxiety?

A. Lets put it this way – you're going to really struggle being both anxious and all panicky within a relaxed body. Just try it if you can! These two states are incompatible. So, yes, relaxation techniques are very important and I'll discuss this in more detail later. In the meantime, why not just try out a 'therapeutic massage' by a professional masseur? Once you've experienced it, you'll realise the benefits of combining both self-induced relaxation techniques (see later) and an externally administered massage.

Q. Can you discuss some of the misconceptions that people have about hypnosis?

A. One of the most common misconceptions that people have is that not everyone can be hypnotised. This is based purely on ignorance and does not reflect the fundamental concept and definition of hypnosis. We all enter, at one level or another, a level of trance or an altered state of awareness in our everyday lives and situations, and at periodic times throughout the day. For example, daydreaming has even been referred to as *waking hypnosis*. It also happens quite often when we're driving the car – we sometimes reach our destination and we are completely or partly oblivious to the intervening period; or when we are reading an interesting novel, time just seems to speed by – a perceptual *time distortion effect*. Conversely, when we are carrying out a boring monotonous task, time seems to drag – an example of a *time expansion effect*. Making love is another example, when your mind becomes more focused! So I hope you can now understand that hypnosis is a very broad phenomenon and not restricted to the performances of a stage hypnotist. It's the generalised aspect of this phenomenon that is used clinically within the scientific and medical fraternity.

Remember that one doesn't have to go into a deep somnambulistic trance to achieve therapeutic results – light or medium stages of trance can suffice in most instances in a clinical therapeutic setting.

Another misconception is that you must either be weak-minded or intellectually very capable to be hypnotised. These suppositions are so far from the truth and no concrete evidence or studies have confirmed this stance. One other which comes to mind, is the possibility of someone remaining in a permanent trance state and being unable to come out! This is impossible and, very importantly, it is you who dictates the rate and depth of the trance that you wish to enter and experience. You can stop the trance process at any time during the procedure. Importantly, you are always in control and the therapist can be regarded as a catalyst in this process of change within the person.

Like I said earlier, the root of many misconceptions is the fear of something that one fails or doesn't wish to understand!

Q. So, am I correct in saying that you really don't have to go into a deep trance state to create that inner, personal change?

A. Yes! Entering a deeper state is no guarantee of achieving a successful therapeutic outcome. A lot of the work is done using the light to medium stages of trance. Some therapists have even found the deeper states of trance to be counterproductive in their therapy work. For our purposes, and for the vast majority of people, the use of a light to medium trance depth should be sufficient.

Q. Does self-hypnosis or any form of self-induced relaxation programme improve with practice?

A. Yes! This principle applies to most things that you'll encounter in life. With continued practice of the various techniques that I'll discuss later, you'll find yourself entering a more progressive, relaxed state of mind and body, much faster than when you first tried the techniques. One should never *try* to enter a deep state, just allow your inner mind – the *unconscious mind* – to dictate the pace and depth of entry. A great deal of therapeutic work can be achieved in a light or medium trance, as I've mentioned earlier. You will find, with time and practice, that deeper states of the mind can be accessed. Not to worry if you can't. What is important is your *motivation* for change. Without this key ingredient, nothing effective and constructive can be achieved!

Q. The idea of doing self-hypnosis or self-induced relaxation sounds really interesting! I imagine it's just a fear of losing your own self-control, especially in front of someone you don't really know. What's your opinion on this matter?

A. I do understand what you are trying to say, but I believe there are some general misunderstandings regarding the matter of who is in control when you experience hypnosis/trance or mental relaxation with the help of a trained hypnotherapist.

Let's make this fact very, very clear. In hypnosis, you *never* actually *lose control!* In fact, if anything, you are more in control of your mind and body, to the extent you permit it to be so. You never lose the control you have. Your misunderstanding is probably due to your media exposure on this subject area and the portrayal of distorted images of the true facts. Let me further add that laypeople and some professionals alike are guilty of being convinced of their own outdated beliefs and opinions – and they are only personal standpoints, not supported by valid experimental studies. Further reading and personal research will reveal to you that hypnosis is a natural *intrinsic phenomenon*, which can be used therapeutically for one's personal well-being.

Q. Does all this (self-hypnosis) take time to achieve?

A. When practising self-hypnosis for personal change, you need to reprogramme your own thinking from, say, a negative or even a neutral mind-set, to one of a more positive frame of mind. This is achieved, as you'll see later, by autosuggesting positive words, thoughts and images, so as to displace any pre-existing negative thought patterns. This does, however, require some time and self-discipline, but you'll find with practice that the whole process is accelerated in the trance state. Every individual is unique and so is the time required to achieve that personal change.

These positive thought processes will be *seeded* deep within your mind and allowed to *grow* and influence your behaviour. Even if the negative thoughts still persist, they won't have the same level of impact. The effects of past negative thoughts and imagery will have been greatly diluted down!

Q. What's the purpose of self-management, if you can go and see a qualified therapist?

A. I would strongly recommend that you see a professional, so that the correct diagnosis can be made and the appropriate personalised, 'tailor-made' advice is provided. Reading a book is no real substitute for a one-to-one consultation with a therapist. The purpose of reading about self-management techniques is to enable you to take some degree of control of your situation. The information provided in a book format should be used in addition to the advice given by a therapist. However, it's not always convenient to see a professional when you need them and they don't always come cheap, but nowadays many are available on the National Health Service – so do make enquiries about it.

Q. What advantages do you see of using hypnosis within the healthcare system?

A. Many! It should play an integral role within the healthcare system. With the adoption and use of a more integrated approach to disease and pathology, the whole treatment process can be accelerated. We should learn from our partners in the East and treat people from a more holistic perspective. We should never underestimate the power of our thoughts to create and influence changes within ourselves. The *placebo response* is a well-recognised effect in the evaluation of the efficacy of various drugs, and is none other than the influence of the mind and thoughts on our bodies.

Considerable savings can be achieved by the employment of such non-invasive techniques in addition to, and the recognition of, the efficacy and treatment goals of the more medically orientated approaches. An infrastructure is required to establish the wider use of clinical hypnosis within the mainstream medical thinking.

Q. What is your opinion of stage hypnotists?

A. I personally admire some of the skills and techniques that they sometimes use in their performances. However, to safeguard the general public, certain ethical considerations should be addressed. Unethical use of hypnosis should be discouraged, and mechanisms put into place by legislation to protect the interests of the ordinary person in the street. In fact, paradoxically, stage hypnotism has done much good in promoting the cause of hypnosis within the minds of many people, including the medical profession. Such entertainment does create much confusion in the minds of people when they fail to see how such use of hypnosis can be used to treat medical conditions or, at the other end of the spectrum, they wrongly assume that hypnosis can be a panacea for all their problems. Also, stage hypnotists are centred around their own egotistical objectives whereas, in hypnotherapy, the therapist's concerns are orientated around the patient's needs and their objectives. It is the patient who is the most important person.

Q. Tell me more about stage hypnosis and hypnotists. I've seen how they have worked on my friend and had him doing all sorts of weird and crazy things. Surely the hypnotist was controlling his mind?

A. I assure you, if that really was the case, this whole world would be run by self-centred, egotistical hypnotists – don't you agree? Okay, let's talk in general terms rather than about a particular individual.

A few points should be kept in mind regarding the volunteers in a stage hypnosis show or act. These people are prepared to perform and their individual personalities lend to this form of theatrical display. They will be selected by the hypnotist only on the basis of their suggestibility. Also, as a result of the stage environment, they will find themselves conforming to the *situational demands* with a considerable degree of *rôle-playing* taking place. Owing to the demands and the situational expectations, the participants will be more prepared than is normal to attribute their strange behaviour patterns to the actions of someone else other than themselves and so feel less embarrassed about the whole situation. Their inhibitions as a consequence are greatly reduced but not eliminated! Importantly, they can refuse to carry out the commands at any time they wish, but are very unlikely to because of their wish to conform! Somehow they will rationalise, at some level within the mind, their continued display of their conforming behaviour patterns.

Q. What is the 'most' important thing a person can learn in trying to cope with anxiety and stress?

A. I think we should first try, briefly, to define what stress and anxiety is. Stress is an emotional and psychological state of mind produced by a stressor – which is any form of stimulus capable of disturbing your physical and mental balance – and so can result in some form of a physiological response. It is a state of psychological tension. Anxiety is the *adaptive response* to stress and often represents an unpleasant emotional state.

However, you should remember, that just as love, hate, happiness, beauty, and so on, mean different things to different people, so does stress. So defining stress (and anxiety) is not very easy. In fact, the terms anxiety and stress are sometimes used interchangeably to convey the same subjective feelings and emotions.

Coming back to the initial question, it is the ability and technique to induce a state of self-relaxation and the associated altered state of mind, that is important in the management of anxiety and stress. This self-management tool is the key to accelerated recovery and personal change. You can use this therapeutic tool wherever and whenever you desire, and in any situation. People have simply forgotten how to relax over the ages and these techniques (which will be discussed later) simply put you back in touch and in control of your inner self!

Q. What causes someone to be anxious?

A. I don't think there is a precise answer to this question. The answer that I'm going to give is a general one – it's multifactorial. By that I mean that there are many factors that might have contributed to the condition. For example, early family and social influences, a genetic predisposition, environmental factors, and so on. What we are concerned with here, however, is how to *control* and *manage* the symptoms, and not the chain of events and the various past situations that might have contributed to creating and sustaining the maladaptive responses.

What anxious people tend to do is to focus on the negative aspects of a particular situation, which then becomes a self-fulfilling prophecy. By not allowing themselves to reframe the situation in a positive way, the negative mind-set maintains and controls the fear within them, making them more susceptible to stress, anxiety and panic type symptoms.

Q. So what type of behaviour pattern would an anxious person exhibit?

A. Well, they'll avoid the anxiety-producing situation(s) rather than confront it head on. In time, the symptoms will probably just worsen, with increasing amounts of anxiety and fear, as the *avoidance behaviour pattern* takes root them.

Q. Is stress and anxiety a common problem?

A. Stress has always been with us since the beginning of time – from the days when early primitive man hunted dinosaurs for food, or was it the other way around? So being stressed and feeling anxious about certain situations are not the real problems in themselves. It's how we interpret the events and deal with them that is important, and not just the events themselves.

The level and type of stress- and anxiety-producing situations do change and fluctuate in each time period and is, basically, in a state of flux. For example, what we are seeing nowadays is the rapid breakdown of the nuclear family in many different cultures worldwide, which has produced a cascade effect of associated problems, stresses and anxieties at sociocultural levels. Another example is the changing roles and expectations of both men and women, with direct and/or indirect relevance to employment and economic opportunities, and the general competitiveness and rivalry between the sexes.

The false belief instilled into us from a young age of being a failure if you do not succeed in life is very much a stress-producing causal factor. This negative attitude can only serve to upset the delicately balanced mental equilibrium and increase the anxiety to perform well within the individual. Now, not all types of stress can be regarded as bad, and some can be quite useful, creating the necessary mental tone and focus within ourselves to successfully complete a certain task or goal. It's when the stress becomes too much owing to our lack of coping strategies, and the resulting anxiety begins to control us, that we should begin to re-evaluate the whole situation. By being able to control the stresses and anxieties, rather than the other way around, you'll be able to use more of the resources of your mind to achieve the required outcome, and with the minimum of time and wasted energy!

Q. So if I understand you correctly, are you saying that some anxiety is beneficial for an individual?

A. Yes! There is an optimum level of anxiety, beyond which it becomes a problem and counterproductive to the individual. Let me put this another way. A little bit of anxiety improves your concentration and mental focus on a problem but, when that anxiety goes beyond a certain critical point for the individual, then the very same anxiety begins to work against you disturbing your own personal *mental calm*. You then begin to lose control of the situation and might, as a consequence, begin to panic – severely compromising your expected performance.

In fact, as far as stress is concerned, there are both positive and negative aspects to it. Did you know that too little excitation can lead to boredom and actually cause stress! On the other hand, too much excitation produces the same result. Both are detrimental to your general well-being. It should be kept in mind that everyone is unique and so will react differently to the various stressors that they may be exposed to, but it is important to remember that everyone needs a little bit of excitement in their lives! Where some will find a situation very stressful, others may look upon it as challenging and even rewarding. It all depends on how one perceives an event. Obviously, personality and sociocultural influences play their roles in understanding human responses to a situation. Remember, it is the *perceived* danger that will dictate the magnitude of the anxiety response.

Q. What are some of ther bodily symptoms of stress and anxiety?

A. Whenever we are confronted with a real or a self-imagined, threatening situation, we tend to show certain physiological and psychological signs and symptoms. There is a real psychosomatic component to this whole process. Let me elaborate on this matter a little more.

The kind of changes that may be exhibited are restlessness and trembling; breathing irregularities, for example, hyperventilation; a feeling of tiredness and a general lack of energy; a *thumping* and *racing heart* with an elevated blood pressure; feelings of dizziness, nausea and sickness; increased sweating; dryness of the mouth; constipation or diarrhoea; and the so-called *butterflies in the stomach*. In addition to these physical symptoms, the individual may also suffer from

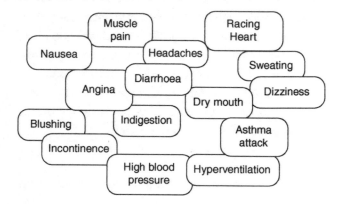

Figure 2: A list of some of the symptoms associated with stress and anxiety

impaired memory, concentration and judgement. Although these feelings and symptoms are not very pleasant, they do serve a function. They, in fact, help us to recognise an uncomfortable and perhaps a dangerous situation, and so prepare us to take an evasive, neutral, or offensive course of action. Look upon it as our own sophisticated early warning radar system! By, say, avoiding a situation and following an evasive route, we are consciously or unconsciously attempting to reduce the stress and the associated anxieties. The most important thing that one should recognise and ask is whether it is the most appropriate response to adopt under the circumstances? Unfortunately, for some, it isn't. They are the people that may benefit with certain *coping strategies* in addition to, if found necessary, *drug intervention*. Obviously, the doctor will be able to advise on the most appropriate drug therapy to pursue.

Diarrhoea – a symptom of anxiety and stress!

Q. What steps can you take to try and overcome some of these anxiety symptoms?

A. I shall explain this in much greater depth later on, but what you can do, in the meantime, is to reframe the anxiety- and stress-producing situation as a personal challenge and, therefore, lessen its threat potential. Alternatively, and circumstances permitting, avoid the anxious situation until you've learnt how to cope with it. Importantly, *avoidance behaviour* should be regarded as only a temporary measure, rather than a long-term or permanent solution.

Sharing your feelings with a close friend or a relative will help you to get the matter into the open, and you might feel much better for it. At least try it! You'll find women are much better at doing this type of personal therapy than men are, but don't ask me why! You may even surprise yourself and benefit from the advice they provide. Bottling up your emotions and feelings will only aggravate the matter. We all need an outlet valve, and relaxation techniques, to be discussed later, are very useful and important in the management and dissipation of the intensity of symptoms.

As a rule of thumb, you should always say things in a positive manner to yourself and avoid the use of negative statements because they will only serve to lower your self-esteem and make you more vulnerable to the stresses of life. Let me give you an example: you should not say: 'I'm going to fail my driving test' – this is a negative statement. You should *reframe* the situation and say something like: 'I'm going to allow myself to remain relaxed and focused throughout the driving session. Whatever the outcome, I shall accept it and learn from it.' What you've done in this latter approach is to omit the two key negative words that frighten many people: *fail* and *test*. The use of positive words triggers off the programming of the subconscious mechanisms within the mind, resulting in a more successful and desired outcome. Learn to accept a particular situation, be it good or bad, and see how you can improve on it! Always autosuggest what you want to achieve, rather than dwell on the negative(s), and always make sure that these autosuggestions are *realistic* and *attainable*.

Let me provide you with another example. The one thing you should never do if you are attending an interview for a job, which you're very nervous about, is to say: 'I'm not going to be nervous ...' This, believe it or not, is the wrong approach and will make matters worse. The key negative word 'nervous' should be omitted and the following autosuggestion tried: 'I'm going to remain relaxed, alert, focused and optimistic ...' You should, firstly, accept the fact that you may feel nervous and uneasy – a completely natural response. Once you've accepted the situation, then go about learning the necessary techniques to minimise the uneasiness of the situation, i.e. the interview in this particular example. As a consequence, you will find that you're much calmer and relaxed generally by accepting your circumstance(s), and so provide a good, solid foundation for internal change (which is then reflected in your external behaviour patterns).

It's sometimes useful to remember the eastern philosophy of not fighting or resisting the particular situation – a principle used in many martial arts techniques – but allowing yourself to go with the flow, so allowing opportunities and changes to occur, evolve and be created, with the minimum amount of wasted mental and physical energy.

Q. I know now that anxiety involves a certain degree of fear of some sort. So what is a phobia?

A. Again, this is an example of an *adaptive response* to a stress-producing situation. It is an extreme, irrational fear of a particular situation or object. This very often results in avoidance behaviour. It must be noted that this condition is not like the *normal* fear expressed by many of us at one time or another. It is more intense and focused, and tends to be more chronic in nature. Examples of phobias include: social phobia (anxiety in social situations); astraphobia (fear of thunder and/or lightening); agoraphobia (fear of open spaces);

uranophobia (fear of homosexuality); phantasmophobia (fear of ghosts), and so on.

Q. What is your opinion regarding the use of drugs in the treatment of anxiety and stress?

A. Over the last decade or so there has been a gradual change in the attitude towards prescription drugs, such as hypnotics and anxiolytics, for these clinical conditions. There has been a distinct shift in favour of using *coping strategies* and various other psychological tools, such as cognitive therapy and hypnosis. The advantages of using these alternative methods are that you don't suffer from the side effects and the dependency potential of using such drugs. There is another issue of the *misuse* and *abuse* of drugs which is becoming an increasing social problem and is of governmental concern. By controlling and reducing the use of drugs you'll be helping, although not eliminating totally, to minimise this area of concern.

Realistically the problem with drug therapy alone, without the psychological interventions, is that you're taking the element of control away from the individual. The main aim and objective of the treatment should be to give back the control to the person. They should be taught the required techniques to cope with the anxiety or stress-producing situation(s), or otherwise, on the cessation of drug therapy, they will be faced with the same situational or presenting problems. We must be very careful not to leave a mental void in such vulnerable individuals. Remember that drugs are not a substitute for real psychological therapy. They only deal with the symptoms and not the causes, providing only temporary relief. Very often, the patients may also develop *tolerance* to the medication(s). What do you do then? Do you then increase the strength of the drugs or use a cocktail of medicines to counterbalance these tolerance effects?

I believe that once the coping strategies are in place then patients should be gradually weaned off their medication. This should be the aim of any successful therapeutic intervention.

Q. Why do doctors prescribe so many of these drugs if some of them are addictive and with many side effects?

A. The answer to this question is not a very straightforward one. Many of the patients and their family members are looking for miracle cures. They expect a quick *fix* to the minor and major stresses of life, and this naive attitude is exhibited in the consulting rooms of many doctors' surgeries. They expect, and on certain occasions demand, that their doctors prescribe them a *magic pill* for their ills! Regretfully, this supply on demand attitude only perpetuates the sad drug-orientated culture that we live in. However, attitudes are now gradually changing amongst healthcare professionals and they are moving towards a more integrated and multidisciplinary management approach. This will certainly be, as far as the financial considerations are concerned, a more cost-effective solution in the long term.

Q. What are the side effects of some of the prescribed medications?

A. This partly depends upon which drugs you are prescribed and your general health and age. Another important factor to be taken into consideration is the interaction with any other medication(s) you might be taking for any other medical condition(s), besides the presenting symptoms of stress and anxiety.

A group of drugs called the *benzodiazepines* are still used to treat anxiety and insomnia and you can become dependent on these drugs, even after a short term of treatment. They do have the tendency to cause daytime drowsiness, and can impair judgement and manual dexterity. This in turn can lead to more accidents, especially in the frail and elderly.

For a more specialist account, you should refer to the many books written about drug therapy in treating stress and anxiety states – which is outside the scope of our discussion.

Q. What are the 'techniques' that one can use to deal with stress and anxiety?

A. The answer to this question is contained in section two of this book (*Management Techniques for Stress and Anxiety*) and so brings this section to a neat close. All the theory you need to know, I believe, has been adequately addressed for you to appreciate the techniques discussed in the following section. Furthermore, you may still require the guidance of a trained professional.

SECTION TWO

MANAGEMENT TECHNIQUES
FOR STRESS AND ANXIETY

INTRODUCTION

It is recommended that you first read through the whole of this section before embarking on the individual practical exercises. You will find, as you read through this section, a considerable overlap between the various techniques that will be described and it is hoped that with appropriate perseverance and practice, you will be able to choose the correct combination of methods to suit your own personal requirements. Take things step by step and do not hurry the natural process of change within yourself.

Initially, you might find that you cannot remember the 'method', and so you could record the exercises, and play the tape back (with suitable pauses incorporated throughout the recording). You could also have a close friend read out the procedure aloud. Adopt and follow the style which suits you best. With practice, you will find that you'll rely less and less on these external aids.

OBJECTIVES

The objectives of this section can be summarised as follows:

- To quickly introduce you to the various coping strategies.

- To create a flexible approach to dealing with stress and anxiety.

- To allow you to mix and match the various techniques (discussed shortly).

- To lay down the foundations of self-awareness and so lead to personal inner change.

THE REFRAMING TECHNIQUE

This is a very important tool that will help you to cope with whatever life has to throw at you! Basically, it involves looking at and dealing with the various situations from a positive stance or mind-set. By allowing yourself to switch to this more positive frame of mind, you are, in fact, programming your subconscious for success, and at the same time laying down the strong foundations for future progress and change.

By changing the way you interpret an event or situation, you will effect a change in the way that any feelings and emotions are attached to it. As a result of this change, your behaviour, response and attitude will also change. It is as simple as that! This is a very powerful and therapeutic means of creating core changes in an individual. In fact, the majority of people who show an inward and outward calm and contentment, display this reframing process quite naturally in their lives, allowing

The 'reframing' technique.

them to develop their own unique resourcefulness to its full potential.

Provided below are some examples to elucidate the points that have been made above:

- NEGATIVE STATEMENT:

  'I'm bored with my room!'

- POSITIVE STATEMENT:

  'What do I need to do to make my room more lively and interesting to live in?'

- NEGATIVE STATEMENT:

  'I don't like the comments my colleague comes out with sometimes.'

- POSITIVE STATEMENT:

  'I'm going to try and understand what makes her come out with such comments.'

- NEGATIVE STATEMENT:

  'I'm sick and tired of my faulty telephone!'

- POSITIVE STATEMENT:

  'It's about time I looked for a new designer telephone to match the décor.'

- NEGATIVE STATEMENT:

  'I'm so fat and ugly.'

- POSITIVE STATEMENT:

  'I'm going to take the necessary steps to reduce my weight by healthy eating and exercise. This will allow me to feel and become more healthy.'

In summary, it is the use of the *positive suggestions* and a determination to change that will enable an individual to proceed from a negative to a more positive state of mind.

THE USE OF POSITIVE SUGGESTIONS IN SELF-HYPNOSIS

The important points (indicated below) will allow you to make better use of suggestions for your own personal benefit, enabling a constructive mental reprogramming to take place naturally. When using self-

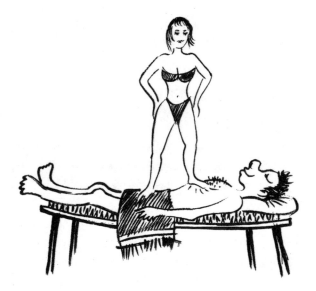

The use of positive suggestions in self-hypnosis!

hypnosis, you will rely upon your own ability to tailor-make the suggestions to suit your own individual requirements and, hence, be more effective.

1. The use of positive, and the avoidance of negative, statements and phrases (for example, the words *can't* or *impossible*) should not be used. Reframe (see the previous section on *The Reframing Technique*) every situation and the associated phrases in a positive context.

2. Use sentences that are clear, unambiguous, short, and easy to say and remember.

3. All suggestions made should be such that they are *realistic* and *achievable*. Do not use suggestions that cannot be realised, as you will be setting yourself up for failure.

4. The more you focus on your particular autosuggestion, the greater the probability that it will be realised.

5. The attachment of a strong *positive emotion* to your suggestion will tend to make that suggestion more effective.

6. Always use the present tense when you are constructing suggestions.

The above points will be appreciated more fully when you begin to practise the various techniques indicated later in this section.

CONTROLLED DEEP BREATHING TO ACHIEVE PHYSICAL RELAXATION AND MENTAL CALM

INTRODUCTION

The method outlined below is very important to master should you wish to create a change within yourself. The technique allows you to take control of your mind and body, which is very important when you are experiencing a panic or anxiety attack. By taking a conscious control of your breathing, you are creating positive physiological changes within your body and mind, with the release of *feel-good chemicals* (endorphins) within your system.

When you are anxious, panicky or even stressed, you have a tendency to induce in yourself shallow, irregular breathing patterns, which in some cases may lead to hyperventilation, dizziness and fainting. By switching to this technique of controlled breathing, you will be counteracting and breaking the negative cycle of the consequences of the anxiety and panic attacks. In fact, very simply, when you adopt this deep, calm breathing, messages are sent back to your *command centre* – the brain – suggesting calmness, and this acts as a cue for further relaxation!

Controlled deep breathing to achieve physical relaxation and mental calm.

With practice, you will very soon realise how calm and relaxed you can feel, creating a pleasant change in your mood and emotions. The two states of arousal and relaxation cannot co-exist! Also, you will find that you will begin to feel more healthy and content with yourself as a consequence of this relaxation technique.

METHOD

1. Sit comfortably with your back straight and supported in a chair, or lie down on your back on the floor, with your legs straight and uncrossed, and your arms resting on either side with the palms of your hands facing downwards.

2. Allow your neck, shoulder and arms to relax, and then allow that relaxation to spread throughout the body. You don't want to be too relaxed so as to feel tired and sleepy!

3. Now, begin to breathe in through the nose, as deeply and comfortably as you can. As you do so, allow your abdominal regions (i.e. stomach regions) to expand as much as possible. Also, at the same time, allow your chest muscles to remain relaxed so they do not rise with each in-breath.

4. Hold your breath for 3 seconds.

5. Now, breathe out through your mouth, slowly and gradually and as you do so, pull your abdominal muscles in so as to flatten your stomach. (Breathe as much air out as is comfortable and possible. With practice, you will find it becomes easier and automatic.)

6. Hold for 3 seconds and then breathe in as in (3) above.

7. Repeat this cycle of breathing, (3) to (6) above, every day for, say, 5 minutes and then gradually increase to 10, 15, 20 minutes, and so on.

NOTES

- Always keep your medicines and inhalers to hand if you suffer from some kind of respiratory condition.

- This technique can be used with your own natural self-hypnosis (see later).

- This technique is practical and easy to use in any anxiety and stressful situation(s). It is obvious that this is not the ideal method of breathing in normal everyday circumstances. The success lies in the flexibility of this approach, and its modification to suit your own body needs and situational circumstances.

THE TECHNIQUE OF SELF-HYPNOSIS

INTRODUCTION

The technique outlined below will teach you to achieve a quick and easy approach to induce relaxation in both body and mind. There are several different methods that can be employed but only one is indicated below. After some considerable practice and experience, you might wish to adapt and change the technique to suit your own personal requirements.

The advantage of learning this method is that it quickly puts you in touch with your *inner being* and awareness, and is simply a very relaxing and an enjoyable experience. At no point through this process should you wish to try and fall asleep. This is not what your aim should be, and can be counterproductive to your own personal objectives. You should allow your mind to exist between the two states of being totally awake and asleep, and you will begin to appreciate and understand this point more fully when you begin to practise self-hypnosis regularly on a daily basis.

(Note: Throughout the text, the word self-hypnosis and self-induced relaxation have been used interchangeably to refer to the same process of accessing inner awareness.)

The technique of self-hypnosis!

METHOD

1. Sit comfortably in a safe place where you will not be disturbed. Your arms and head should be comfortably supported. The legs should be uncrossed, with both feet resting on the floor, so as to prevent any pins and needles developing, as you begin to enter a more relaxed state of body and mind (see below).

   For beginners, make sure you are wearing comfortable clothing so that the peripheral blood flow is not impeded in any way. With time and practice, you will notice that clothing and other factors (e.g. external noise) are no longer nuisance factors in entering your own unique trance. Also, good sitting posture is very important so as to prevent any unnecessary stresses and strains to the body (e.g. to the spine).

2. Set a time limit of, say, 20 to 30 minutes, by using an alarm clock or a wrist-watch. Make sure they are to hand, so that the alarm can be quickly de-activated when the time period is over.

3. Now, focus on a distant, non-moving point above eye-level (like a fixed point on a ceiling) and just allow your eyes to close when you are ready to do some *inner work*, or just simply relax.

   As you breathe *in*, allow yourself to imagine that

you are breathing in *calmness* and *serenity* into your body. And as you breathe *out*, imagine you are breathing out all the accumulated *tensions* and *strains* from within your body. Just enjoy the experience (see the previous section on *Controlled Deep Breathing*).

4. Now, allow yourself to focus your mind internally on a comfortable and relaxed part of your body, and allow this relaxation to expand throughout your body.

5. As the process in (4) above is taking place, give yourself appropriate autosuggestions simultaneously (see section on *The Use of Positive Suggestions in Self-hypnosis* and *The Reframing Technique*).

   For example:

   'I am feeling more calm and relaxed as the time goes on ...'

   'I am enjoying the experience of experiencing the calmness that exists ... flowing into me ... through me ... and out of me ... with each breath I take ... knowing that positive, beneficial changes are taking place within me ... at both mind and body level ... at this very moment in time ...'

   'I am allowing myself to enjoy this quiet period of relaxation ... knowing that I am in the safe capable hands of my *inner being* ... the subconscious ... allowing it to guide me ... inside and outside of my *conscious awareness* ...'

Should you wish to feel more confident about yourself, just allow your mind to drift to a period in your life when you were more confident or, alternatively, create a fantasy situation where you are and feel more calm, relaxed and confident about yourself. Similarly, for a pleasant experience, just allow your mind to drift to a period in your life when you actually experienced that particular situation. You will surprise yourself on how your feelings can change, and how relaxed you can become as a result of this exercise.

6. Now, when the alarm goes off (after the designated time period), just calmly turn it off and gradually begin to reorientate yourself to a full wakeful consciousness. As you do so, you may wish to give yourself the following autosuggestion: 'As I begin to reorientate myself to the here and now ... I am feeling mentally alert and yet calm ... relaxed and in control ...'

Allow your eyes to open (if they are not open already), and take a few deep breaths. Stretch your arms and legs, and just enjoy what you've experienced.

NOTES

- It is recommended that you practise this method twice a day on a regular basis for, say, 10 to 20 minutes.

- The use of *controlled deep breathing* will facilitate deeper relaxation and calmness, and allow you to control your bodily functions more readily. Its use with the above method will deepen the experience you can attain with self-hypnosis.

- Very rarely will you be blessed with a noise-free environment. So any external noises, like the sound of motor cars, aeroplanes and children, etc., can be incorporated into your own unique trance experience. Never mentally *fight* against such forces but always work with them. For example, considering the noise of an overflying aeroplane, you may wish to incorporate it into your trance by saying the following silently and mentally: 'I will allow the sound of the aircraft to relax me even further ... feeling more and more relaxed ... as the sound fades away into the distance ...', and so on.

- When using autosuggestions in the trance, try to picture what you are suggesting to yourself, and make it very interesting. *Feel* it and *hear* it, etc. What is important is that you make use of all your senses to create the desired mental outcome.

- Gentle massage of the temples in step (3) above (e.g. by a friend or partner) will facilitate the process.

- With time and practice, you will be able to switch into your own unique trance modes and create your own virtual reality scenarios in your mind's imagination. You will need to establish at what times of the day is the best time for you to practise self-hypnosis, for example, why not use your own natural breaks throughout the day? They do not have to be long – 10 minutes can be quite sufficient!

- Relaxing background music will facilitate the trance experience.

THOUGHT STOPPING TECHNIQUE

INTRODUCTION

The principle involved in this technique is the breaking of the chain of negative, non-productive thoughts. By acting in an inhibitory manner it allows more positive thinking patterns to be established in the individual.

Many individuals who suffer from anxiety and panic attacks allow the negative chain of thoughts to surface and dominate their normal thinking processes, displacing any positiveness that might exist at that moment in time. These negative thoughts become s e l f - f u l f i l l i n g prophecies, which lead on to negative outcomes and so lower your self-esteem even further. The method below shows how such negative processes (i.e. unrealistic, unproductive and anxiety arousing) can be interrupted and be replaced with a more positive reality.

Thought stopping technique!

METHOD

1. Close your eyes.

2. Think of or verbalise a negative thought sequence which troubles you. For example, 'I'm going to have a panic attack.'

3. Then stay *STOP!*

Picture this word, bright and colourful, occupying your complete *imaginary visual field*. You may, if you wish, accompany this with some appropriate sound or music within your imagination.

4. Take a few, slow, deep breaths and allow general muscle relaxation – especially around the shoulders and neck regions. (You will find when you're anxious and stressed that the muscles around your shoulders and neck become quite taut and tense. This reaction in itself will send signals to your brain about an impending *perceived* danger, causing an inappropriate arousal response. Therefore, we need to prevent or substantially reduce this initial response to achieve our objectives.)

5. Open your eyes and think about something else. You may wish to think about the person you would *realistically* like to be under those circumstances, for example the more confident you!

6. Now, say to yourself something positive about that particular situation. For example: 'Come what may, I am coping, like I've always done in the past. I will learn from this experience.'

7. Repeat the above procedure several times.

NOTES

- It is natural for negative thoughts to return but when they do return you must interrupt them with positive ones. With time and practice your positive thought patterns will become automatic, displacing the negative pattern(s) that have previously controlled or influenced you. Once established, you will have laid down the foundations for change for yourself. You will find that the negative thoughts will return less and less, until they no longer have such a strong impact on you.

- Remember, your positive thoughts should be realistic and achievable.

- The above technique is successfully employed by many students who feel anxious and nervous about sitting exams, etc.

NATURALISTIC SELF-INDUCED RELAXATION

INTRODUCTION

The method outlined below provides a quick, easy and convenient way to get in touch with your inner self when you need to. This method can be adapted and amended with the other techniques described in this book to suit your individual needs.

METHOD

1. When you feel that you need to take a break from a particular task or situation, or just need some time to yourself, for whatever reason(s), just allow your eyes to close. Mentally set yourself a suitable time period (e.g. 10 or 20 minutes).

2. Modulate your breathing to a slow and gentle cycle, becoming progressively more relaxed.

3. Focus on any comfort in your body. Now, imagine this comfort expanding throughout your body, paying particular attention to your shoulders and neck muscles.

4. As you begin to relax even further, just allow your *unconscious mind* to carry out both physical and psychological healing outside your own *conscious awareness*. You may wish to incorporate the following autosuggestion: '... allowing my unconscious mind to carry out required physical and psychological healing ... in harmony with my conscious awareness ...'

5. Now, allow yourself to drift back to full wakeful consciousness (after your designated time period). You may wish to incorporate the following autosuggestion as you return to conscious awareness: '... feeling more calm ... more refreshed ... mentally alert and in control ...

knowing that my unconscious mind is working on my behalf ... outside of my normal conscious awareness ...'

NOTES

- You may wish to practise *controlled breathing* in stage (2) above. This depends upon how much time you have set aside and how deep a trance you wish to experience.

- During stage (3) above you may wish to associate the spreading relaxation with a *healing white light or mist* which diffuses throughout your body. Alternatively, some prefer to use colours to facilitate this process. Be as creative as you wish to be!

MENTAL VISUALISATION TO IMPROVE YOUR PERFORMANCE

INTRODUCTION

This is a very simple, but a powerful technique to create both internal and external changes, creating new behaviour patterns and/or modifying existing ones. As in most cases, when hypnotic interventions are used, it relies on the imagination of the individual and their innate ability to create appropriate visual imagery.

Don't forget that a mental picture is worth a thousand words! We very often create a picture in our minds first and then use words to describe it – rather than the other way around.

In the method outlined below, you will be asked to mentally visualise scenes of the person you wish to be, and then be asked to act it out in your mind. The purpose of this technique is to reprogramme your mind from a negative to a more positive mind-set. With continued practice, you will be able to carry out physically the more appropriate and positive things you imagined and thought about. Let's put this another way. You will come across people who tend to dwell on the negative aspects of life. What this does is to reinforce or introduce a negative, counterproductive programme of thinking to your mind. This is then unfortunately acted out at a behavioural level and, thus, becomes a self-fulfilling prophecy leading to a less than satisfactory performance.

You will find that most actors, performers, musicians, sportsmen/sportswomen, etc., use this technique of *mental visualisation* and *rehearsal* in one form or another to achieve their desired goal(s). When the results aren't satisfactory, they learn from this *feedback* – no such thing as failure in their terminology – and reintroduce an amended visual mental imagery to act upon. This process is repeated several times and this

Mental visualisation to improve your performance!

mental image is fine-tuned until the appropriate results are obtained. It is as simple as that!

We all visualise at some level but some are better than others. You may experience some initial teething problems but do not give up on this method (described below). Persevere and enjoy the fruits of your hard work!

METHOD

1. Either:

    (a) Induce a trance state in yourself (see section on *The Technique of Self-hypnosis*); or

    (b) Recognise your own personal quiet moment. This normally occurs every 90–120 minute cycles (Ultradian rhythm) – discussed later.

2. Choose a situation that you wish to improve upon or change completely. For example, an interview, an invitation to a party that you're uneasy about or working with a colleague.

3. Now, *imagine* the person you want to be in that particular situation you have chosen. You may find this difficult to imagine. If this is the case, then try selecting a *rôle model* and in your imagination try adopting his or her position, attitudes, mannerisms, and so on.

4. Run a *dummy sequence* of the events through your mind, with you *observing yourself*, as if on a television or cinema screen. (This is sometimes referred to as being in the *dissociated position*, whereby you see everything from a second position, as opposed to experiencing it yourself – the so-called *associated position*). Like a director of a movie, run the imagined sequence from the beginning of your selected problem situation to its end. Fine-tune any

behaviour patterns you would like to change in yourself. See what other changes you would like to make, for example, your clothing, your hairstyle, etc.

5. Now, run the same sequence as in (4) above but this time allow yourself to step *into* yourself in this imagined situation and experience everything that is happening to you – the feelings, emotions, etc. Fine-tune *in* any feelings, etc. and just experience the whole situation unfolding before your very eyes. (This is what is called the *associated position* – you feel, see, smell and hear everything as if it is really happening to you.)

6. Repeat (5) above, as frequently as is required, before the actual anticipated event – at *least* once a day for five consecutive days before the event or problem situation.

NOTES

- Before you decide to try out the method above, you may wish to try the following mental exercise to appreciate what is expected of you.

  Select the most recent thing you've done, say, a few minutes earlier, like, making a cup of tea. Just visualise from a *dissociated position* making the tea, that is, seeing yourself walking into the kitchen, filling the kettle with water, and so on. Once you have done that, then run the same sequence in the *associated position*, where you are actually experiencing everything, and seeing everything as it was, and even notice things you've not noticed before. Repeat this procedure with other situations which you've done recently (e.g. a recent session of passionate lovemaking!). Again, you may wish to add or subtract certain scenes and events from your imagery to fine-tune it to your own personal requirements.

- The greater the *associated* experience and the more *realistic* the imagined situation is, the more probable will be the desired outcome that you are seeking.

- Always prepare a back-up plan in your imagined sequence, just in case things do not go according to plan in the *real world*. For example, if a person makes an unexpected sarcastic remark, then go to 'plan B' to counteract the remark and to regain control of the situation. Do not let it take you by surprise. Be prepared to introduce these safety measures into your mental rehearsal of events, once you've run the initial imaginary sequence two or three times in your mind. Just trust the use of your imagination and your inner intuitive self!

THE ANCHORING TECHNIQUE

INTRODUCTION

The *anchoring process* is a simple and practical technique that makes use of mental associations by using feelings of, say, calmness, confidence and relaxation, linked to an external physical, bodily *trigger* (see *Knight, 1995; O'Connor and Seymour, 1990*). For example, a mental association of calmness when you join your middle finger with your thumb, i.e. the physical trigger. Once this so-called *anchor* is established, you can use it in many different circumstances that require you to access those feelings associated with that particular anchor. For example, in situations of anxiety, you can trigger the physical anchor of calmness and relaxation and notice how your feelings change as a consequence, enabling you to enter a more positive frame of mind.

The 'anchoring' technique!

An example of this process occurring in our every day lives is when we recognise a familiar scent (e.g. a perfume – the *anchor*) which *triggers* a number of mental associations linked with that scent, and so allowing memories to flood back into our conscious awareness. It is as simple as that!

METHOD

1. Close you eyes and allow yourself to relax. Take a few deep, slow breaths to facilitate your inner and outer relaxation.

2. Now, *think* about a time in the past when you had those feelings that you would like to access and use in your present situation or circumstance. If you are having some difficulty in remembering the situation, then simply make one up, or think of someone who has those desired attributes.

3. Now, choose an *anchor* that you wish to use. The example we used above was the joining of the middle finger to the thumb. Another example of an anchor may be to make a clenched fist of one or both of the hands. There are so many different types of anchor you can use but always choose the one with which you are comfortable.

4. Now, allow your mind to drift back in time to a period where those feelings that you wish to access once existed (see [2] above). This time, rather than

thinking about that particular moment in time, allow yourself to be immersed in the imaginary situation. Experience all those feelings and use all your senses to be aware of the things happening to you in your imagination. For example, what are you seeing? What are you hearing? What are you smelling? What can you feel at both an emotional and a physical tactile level?

In other words, you must be within your imagined body and be *looking out* at your *perceived* world and experiencing all the feelings and emotions of that particular situation in the past. This is what is commonly termed as being in the *associated state* (as mentioned earlier in the section on *Mental Visualisation to Improve your Performance*). You should not be *viewing yourself* in your imagined situation – the *dissociated state* – as this will not generate the emotions and feelings that are required in this technique. You must be aiming to *live out* the whole experience or fantasy once again.

5. When the emotions and feelings that you wish to access reach their *peak*, then touch your middle finger with your thumb, or use any other suitable anchor that you have chosen, as discussed above. Hold this anchor for as long as the desired emotions and feelings are reaching *their peak*. Once the emotions have reached their peak, *release your*

anchor by – in our particular example – separating the thumb and finger. This is very important and the timing is very critical! The thumb and finger should not be held together once the required emotions are gradually subsiding, *after* reaching their peak.

6. Now, open your eyes immediately and think about something else. Move to a different physical location. Stretch your arms and legs.

7. Repeat (1) to (6) above to reinforce and fine-tune the mental associations with your particular anchor.

8. Now, check the technique you have just followed to see if it really works, as follows:

   (a) Think of something unrelated to your particular problem situation.

   (b) Now, quickly, bring your finger and thumb together, or any other anchor you have been using – referred to as *firing the anchor* in some literature.

   (c) Notice the associated feelings you have been working on flood back to your conscious awareness.

   If, however, *firing the anchor* does not produce the desired result, then simply repeat the sequence (1) to (6) above until you're successful!

9. Now, close your eyes and allow yourself to drift to

a period in time in the *future* (i.e. imagine the future situation) which will require your anchor to be used. For example, meeting someone at a future event about which you feel very anxious and nervous. Just allow yourself to feel totally *associated* in the experience (and not *dissociated*). When the anxiety begins to rise, *fire the anchor* at an appropriate time and experience the feelings that you have linked to your particular anchor spread throughout your being. Enjoy the experience and the feelings of being in control, and that you are coping much better with your situation. Once you have done this *dummy run* of a future event, you will pleasantly surprise yourself how much easier it becomes to deal with the actual real life situation when it does arrive and you fire the anchor.

10. Repeat (9) above until all the various images have been fine-tuned and you are content with what you have achieved.

NOTES

- You can strengthen your existing anchor with other anchors (e.g. of calmness, confidence, etc.) by using the fingers of the other hand, or some other *physical trigger*. These will act in synergy with the existing anchor, producing a very powerful result. For example, in creating a second anchor, you repeat the above process from (1) to (7) but when you arrive at steps (8) and (9), you fine-tune both the anchors, instead of just the one anchor. The same principle applies to the creation of multiple anchors.

USING BIORHYTHMS TO ACCESS THE INNER UNCONSCIOUS RESOURCES FOR SELF-IMPROVEMENT

INTRODUCTION

This approach allows the individual to get in touch with their inner self and being – the *creative unconscious*. Just regard it as your intuitive part, that you should respect and listen to for your own personal and psychological well-being. By employing the following technique, you will be using the natural *ultradian rhythm* (see notes below) of the body to its maximum efficiency, and be working with your body and mind in synergy, rather than in opposition.

METHOD

1. Recognise your own, personal, quiet moment. This normally occurs about every 90–120 minutes.

2. On a scale of 0 (minimum) to 10 (maximum), rate your personal discomfort – whatever that may be.

3. Say to yourself: 'When I'm ready to be advised and guided by my inner creative part ... my unconscious mind ... my inner being ... I will allow my eyes to close ... and to receive the deeper messages from within', or something to that effect.

4. After a little time interval – and you will know how long – open a dialogue with your unconscious inner self. Talk to it in a relaxed and a calm manner, by asking it *open-ended* questions. Take your time during this process or otherwise it will be counterproductive. The objective of your questioning is to find *mutually* acceptable ways of obtaining solutions to your personal problem(s). You may wish to try asking the following questions to your creative unconscious:

   • What changes are required of me to cope and deal with my particular situation more effectively?'

   • 'Will you allow my intuitive feelings in a particular situation to be my personal guide?'

   • 'Once you have evaluated my whole situation, will you guide me and allow me to make the required adjustments to effectively reach my objective(s)?', and so on.

5. To bring this period of reflective insight into oneself to an end, you may wish to say the following to yourself: 'When the necessary insights have been made … whether I'm consciously aware of it or not … I will allow my eyes to open … knowing that you … my unconscious part of me … will guide me and protect me … and knowing that the healing process that has started within myself … will continue to grow and blossom *outside my conscious awareness* … as I begin to reorient myself to the here and now … I feel mentally alert … and more calm and relaxed … and in control.'

6. Now, rate your feelings on your initial scale of 0 to 10 and notice the pleasant difference.

NOTES

- Don't be afraid of talking to yourself! We do it all the time in our normal daily activities.

- The ultradian cycle is a natural biological rhythm – a biorhythm – which follows a periodic sequence in a given 24-hour day. The cycle occurs approximately every 90 minutes and influences the alertness and the arousal in the individual. It is during these periods that effective and therapeutic work can be achieved, especially if you require the deeper involvement of your creative unconscious mind (see *Rossi, 1986*).

- Remember that the inner unconscious is responsible for many physiological and psychological processes in a person.

- When you begin this process, it may be easier to focus and concentrate on any relaxed and comfortable part of yourself, and then just to allow the relaxation to spread throughout the body.

- Regard your personal *discomfort* or problem as an indicator of what needs to be addressed to create the new change within yourself.

- When *talking* to your unconscious, always be courteous and respectful. If you're not getting the results or answers you desire, then *negotiate* with it and come up with a *mutually* acceptable alternative(s). You must fully appreciate the importance of this process of negotiation with your unconscious.

- Sometimes, you may not fully understand or appreciate the messages you're receiving from your unconscious. If that occurs, do not worry about it. The unconscious will continue to work for you outside your normal conscious awareness. Strange as it may seem, what you must do is to continue your dialogue with your inner unconscious part, so that it is made fully aware of your position!

ACCESSING THE INNER ADVISER

INTRODUCTION

This is a well-established technique used by many therapists, and many variations of this method have been adopted in clinical work. As you will see below, it enables the individual to give some *form* to their unconscious forces and, thus, enable a meaningful two-way dialogue to take place. The form you create in your imagination is your own unique, personal *inner adviser* – a little like the concept of a *guardian angel!* It can also take the form, if desired, of a human, an animal, an alien, etc., because it's your own personal reality and you decide the form in which it may appear to you. In many respects, it is very similar to the approach discussed above, in negotiating with your own personal, creative unconscious.

Some people find it much easier and effective if initially a therapist takes you through the whole process of accessing your own inner adviser, to be later followed by your own attempt at self-hypnosis.

You will notice some similarities between the method outlined below and other techniques that I have discussed earlier. It is up to you to use a suitable combination of methods to suit your own needs to produce the most effective outcome – a *mix-and-match approach*.

Accessing the inner adviser.

METHOD

1. Adopt either of these two approaches:

   - Induce a trance state in yourself (see section on *The Technique of Self-hypnosis*); or

   - Recognise your own, personal, quiet moment. This normally occurs about every 90 minute cycles (see previous section on *Using Biorhythms*).

2. Now, imagine your *inner adviser* (IA) in a nice, calm and beautiful setting. Trust your imagination to come up with a suitable *form* for the IA. This may take some time, so a little patience may be required on your part during this stage.

3. Now, thank the IA for expressing itself to you in a suitable *form*.

4. Open a dialogue with the IA and say that you wish to share your feelings and problems with it, and that you hope to seek and benefit from any advice that it wishes to share with you (especially regarding your particular problem situation, e.g. the anxiety- and stress-producing situation). It is very important on your part to create a rapport and empathy with the IA. Show that you are genuine and sincere, and are taking the whole matter very seriously.

5. Ask your IA in which way and capacity will it

function in dealing with your problem situation? (Frame your questions in a way that encourages a positive dialogue, obtaining as much information, as possible, and using persuasive and negotiating skills.) Thank the IA for the answer(s) it provides (whether they are to your liking or not!). Always be polite and courteous when communicating with your personal IA to achieve the best results.

You may wish to ask the following questions:

- 'What, in your opinion, is/are the cause(s) of my problem(s)?'

- 'In which ways should I change to enable me to attain my desired outcome?'

- 'What would you like me to do, so that we are *both* happy with the solution/outcome?'

- 'Are there any temporary or permanent advantages in having my present situation?'

- 'Would you like to offer me a minimum of, say, *three alternative solutions* to my present way of handling or dealing with the situation, so that I may give each at least a try. If they are unsuitable, I can always return to my original way of doing things, until we both come up with a more suitable alternative(s).'

- 'Would you like to share any other information with me before I say goodbye?'

6. When bringing this meeting to a close, you may wish to say the following: 'Thank you for sharing with me your wisdom and words of advice. I really appreciate the kindness and help you have provided me. Whenever I need to see you again, I'll just allow myself to travel *down* this same journey into your presence (i.e. the IA). However, should you wish to make yourself known to me, just allow *your being* to drift into my consciousness ...' (Feel free to change and adapt the above dialogue to suit your own needs and personality.)

7. To bring this period of reflective insight into one's self to an end, you can say to yourself the following: 'When the necessary insights have been made ... whether I'm consciously aware of it or not ... I will allow my eyes to open ... knowing that you ... my personal IA (i.e. the unconscious forces) will guide me and protect me ... and knowing that the healing process that has started within myself will continue to grow and blossom *outside my conscious awareness* ... as I begin to reorientate myself to the here and now ... I feel more mentally alert ... and, yet, calm and relaxed ... and in control ...'

Stretch your arms and legs, and just enjoy what you've experienced!

A STRATEGY FOR DEALING WITH INTENSE EMOTIONAL FEELINGS

INTRODUCTION

At certain times during the day you may feel very sensitive, emotional and even very vulnerable, while at other times, less so. Sometimes the feelings of anxiety will arise from nowhere, whereas on other occasions it may be due to a memory of a situation or an incident that acts as a *cue* for your arousal response. Anxiety can be loosely regarded as a hybrid of physiological changes within the body and perceptual changes where unpleasant feelings and thoughts dominate.

The technique described below will teach you to cope

A strategy for dealing with intense emotional feelings!

with the feelings arising from a memory but should not be regarded as a substitute for professional advice and help from a trained practitioner or a therapist. This method will assist you in *reprogramming* your mind with different and therapeutically beneficial thought patterns.

METHOD

1. Take a deep breath and allow your eyes to close comfortably.

2. Select a memory that is troubling you.

3. On a scale of, say, 0 (minimum) to 10 (maximum), rate your own personal discomfort.

4. Notice if you are observing the scene of yourself (*dissociated state*) or actually experiencing the memory by living it out (*associated state*). If you are in the associated state, allow yourself to drift out of your body to view yourself as an *observer*, i.e. to lessen the emotional impact. If you are already in the dissociated state, then that's great!

5. Allow your neck, shoulder and arms to relax, and then allow that relaxation to spread throughout your body.

6. Proceed further with *controlled deep breathing* (see earlier section related to this topic) as you still remain focused on your chosen memory.

7. As you observe your memory sequence (in the *dissociated state*), begin to evaluate the situation with a more critical eye. Breakdown and analyse the situation to see what factors may be perpetuating and sustaining it. You may wish to ask the following questions:

- 'Are my reactions to this situation really appropriate or are there other ways of dealing with this problem?'

- 'What exactly is the problem and what must I do to significantly reduce or eliminate this anxiety-producing situation?'

- 'What coping strategies should I adopt?'

- 'What *suitable* avoidance strategies should I adopt?'

By trying to understand the nature of your *perceived* unpleasant memory, and asking yourself deeper, more searching questions, you will be actively mobilising your *mental machinery* to re-examine the resources that you possess in coping, and even changing the way you *perceive* your anxiety-producing situation. (You might require the help of a very close friend to assist you through this stage.)

8. Now, begin to focus more closely on your disturbing memory, making sure you are still viewing it in the *dissociated state*. Change certain

aspects of your memory, which will in turn change your associated emotional feelings. For example:

- Make the disturbing image small so as to occupy a small rectangular segment of your visual field, preferably in an extreme corner (e.g. the extreme lower left-hand corner). Also, push the image further and further into the distance, making it *hazy* and *blurred*.

- Make the image *less bright* and *dull*.

- If you are viewing in colour, make the image into a *black and white* scene.

- Accompany the memory with some relaxing music or with complete silence.

- If appropriate, make the image a little *humorous*.

Create other changes to the image that you regard as appropriate, so as to reduce the emotional impact that it has on you.

9. Fine-tune the image you have manipulated and altered in (8) above, so that you are content with it.

10. Now, open your eyes and think of something else. Stretch your arms and legs, reverting back to your normal breathing pattern in the process.

11. Now, after about a minute or so, close your eyes once again, and revert back to *controlled breathing*.

Bring back the new image(s), as in (9) above, to your conscious awareness. Once you have done that, open your eyes and think about something different, pleasant, calming and relaxing.

12. Repeat (11) above, 10 times in quick succession to produce the desired results.

13. Now, rate your feelings on your initial scale of 0 to 10, and notice the pleasant difference.

NOTES

- Don't be afraid to spend time on stage (7) above. If this stage seems too difficult now, then proceed to stage (8) and continue as normal. It may mean that you require a therapist to guide you through this stage.

EXERCISE AS A MEANS OF CREATING MENTAL AND PHYSICAL WELL-BEING

INTRODUCTION

Physical exercise is very important for both your physical and mental well-being, with mood enhancement and health-related benefits. The thing that many people do not realise is that physical exercise causes the release of certain chemicals within the body, called *endorphins*, which are partly responsible for the positive mood changes. You should never underestimate the power of regular exercise. Research studies have indicated significant benefits of exercise in people with certain types of depression and those persons inclined to aggressive tendencies.

Exercise as a means of creating mental and physical well-being!

With time and a regular exercise regime, you will begin to feel good about yourself, and so indirectly begin to influence your own personal self-image and self-esteem. And, importantly, you will become healthier, so minimising many of the health risk factors that affect many people today. Don't forget a healthy diet is a must to achieve this goal! Ideally, I would recommend a local gym where a personal fitness trainer will guide you through the training programme. It's a good investment in yourself and at the end of the day you will feel much better for it. However, if you're feeling down and a little miserable, anxious, and stressed, the last thing on your mind will be to go down to your local gym. So why don't you invest – finances permitting – in an exercise bike or a computerised treadmill for yourself?

Outlined below is a method that combines both exercise and trance to achieve a personal therapeutic change.

METHOD

For this technique you will require an exercise bike. The more you are prepared to spend on the bike, the better you will find it in terms of specification. Shop around for one you feel comfortable with.

1. Sit yourself on the bike and allocate 15 to 20 minutes for your exercise programme. (Most bikes

will have a clock that you can set to remind you when your time is up.)

2. Set the bike's *resistance* to the minimum setting.

3. Now, close your eyes and allow a sense of calmness to spread throughout your body – you may wish to synchronise this with your natural breathing cycle. Remember that you are *not* practising deep relaxation in this technique.

4. Now, begin to give yourself positive suggestions, and as you do so, commence pedalling. Gradually at first, and then speeding up to a comfortable pace.

   A possible autosuggestion you may wish to use is: 'I am feeling calmer ... stronger ... and healthier ...' Try visualising these words, flashing at you in your mind's eye, or simply imagine yourself in a situation where your suggestions make sense. It is often said that imagery is worth a thousand words!

5. When your allocated time is over, open your eyes and *gradually* come to a stop. As you do so, *imagine* yourself feeling healthier and give yourself the following autosuggestion: 'I am becoming healthier ... stronger ... and more in control as each day passes ... more calm and mentally alert ... ready to face the various challenges of life ... ' Repeat this autosuggestion a minimum of three times.

NOTES

- When commencing an exercise programme, you should always consult your doctor to make sure it is suitable, especially if you are taking any medicines.

- As mentioned in stage 2 above, it is recommended that initially a minimum resistance setting be used on the bike. With continued practice, you might wish to increase the resistance setting or, alternatively, just increase the exercise time from say, 20 minutes to 30 minutes, and so on. The above method can be nicely adapted to be used with a treadmill.

- The use of relaxing music will facilitate the process. Avoid listening to the radio or your favourite songs, as this will, naturally, disturb your trance experience. You should remain mentally focused on your autosuggestions and avoid any distractions.

- It is very important to keep your breathing steady and regular. Irregular breathing and hyperventilation can make you feel sick and dizzy.

BODY POSTURE TO INDUCE INNER MENTAL CHANGES

INTRODUCTION

Therapists know that there is a mind and body connection, and that a kind of *biofeedback* system operates at one level or another. For example, the posture and stance that you might adopt when sad will be quite different to that adopted when you are happy and excited. It's only natural! So, for our understanding, if when you are happy you deliberately adopt a body posture that you normally adopt when you are feeling down and depressed, you will find that the *happy emotions* will become quite dampened. What is actually happening is that the signals are being sent from the muscles controlling the posture to your brain *saying* that you are sad. This confuses the brain as two incompatible signals now coexist, i.e. the happy and sad states. So what the brain does is to try and find a compromise between these two states, which results in the dampening of the initial emotions. The opposite also holds true: holding a confident posture and stance when you are sad, for example, will produce a change in the emotions. Thoughts do influence our physiology, and vice versa.

The technique outlined below will show you how you can create a *more* positive state of mind when you are feeling emotionally down by simply changing your posture. This coupled with positive autosuggestions should result in a better outcome.

METHOD

1. Take a deep breath. As you breathe in, allow your head to move backwards slightly and your eyes looking upwards. Do not strain yourself. You must remain comfortable and relaxed. And then breathe out.

2. Again, as you breathe in, just straighten and broaden your shoulders.

3. Relax your facial (and jaw) muscles, so as to make you less tense and more calm, and even allow those inner subjective feelings of confidence to emerge and evolve.

4. Practise *controlled deep breathing* (see earlier section on *Controlled Deep Breathing*). However, if this is not appropriate, just take a few slow, deep breaths through your nostrils.

5. *Pretend* to be the calm and the confident person you would like to be. Perhaps, even *model* yourself on someone whom you admire, possessing the qualities you would like to see in yourself! In fact, successful actors are very good at doing this!

NOTES

- In stage (1) above, you were deliberately asked to look up. The reason for this is that by looking up, you are *forced* to access visually constructed and remembered images. It's the way we are programmed. Looking down would access internal feelings, emotions and dialogue – which, in these circumstances we should like to avoid. (A more detailed explanation of eye *movements* in relation to our thought processes is outside the scope of this book.)

MASSAGE AS A THERAPEUTIC TOOL

INTRODUCTION

Body massage is an excellent means of inducing body relaxation and facilitating the release of the *feel good chemicals* within your system. Under the hands of a trained professional it can produce a significant change at both a mind and body level, and just a general feeling of well-being within yourself. It is an excellent aid to releasing negative emotions in many individuals.

It is recommended that you have a whole body massage – finances permitting – at least once a month.

Massage as a therapeutic tool!

We are not talking about a sexual massage here! You need to remain totally focused throughout the session as described in the method section below.

METHOD

1. Explain to the masseur that you will be practising a form of mental meditation which will require a mutual cooperation and a respect for your silence.

2. While lying down, allow yourself to feel totally relaxed, both mentally and bodily, as the masseur begins the session.

3. Allow your mind to drift as the relaxing effects of the massage start to take place.

4. As the mind is drifting, autosuggest suitable, positively framed statements (see section on *The Reframing Technique* and *The Use of Positive Suggestions in Self-hypnosis*). Use all your senses (e.g. visual, touch, auditory, smell, etc.) to create the maximum impact of your suggestions on yourself. Even create your own *virtual reality* situation within your imagination.

5. As the session comes to a close, you may wish to give yourself the following suggestion: '... I will allow my eyes to open, knowing that you ... my unconscious part of me ... is guiding me and protecting me ... and knowing that the healing process that has started within myself is continuing to grow and blossom outside my conscious awareness ... as I begin to reorientate myself to the here and now ... feeling mentally more alert ... calm ... relaxed ... and in control ...'

NOTES

- Request that no sudden or jerky movements be made as this may shock or disturb your meditative state of mind.

- The use of relaxing music, if permitted, will aid and facilitate the process.

- Some people find themselves to be more responsive to suggestion in this deep state of physical and mental relaxation and use this to their own personal advantage.

NASAL BREATHING AS A MEANS OF CHANGING YOUR INTERNAL STATE OF MIND

INTRODUCTION

The brain is traditionally divided into the left and right hemispheres, possessing various overlapping functions. The left hemisphere is believed to be responsible for processing information in an analytical and logical manner, whereas the right hemisphere has a more intuitive, deeper, emotional dimension to it (see Figure 1). (Also, for left-handed people there may be a reversal in the functions of the right and left hemispheres, that is, the right hemisphere is now responsible for the analytical and logical processing.) This demarcation is not absolute, and recent research has indicated that some people may have their mental functions diffusely organized within the brain structure – not complying with the traditionally understood concepts of brain function and anatomical location.

Interestingly, in a small number of cases it has been found that when certain regions of the brain have suffered minor trauma, other regions of the brain can compensate and take over control to serve the same function, and so maintain a delicate balance – *homeostasis* – within the brain system.

Keeping in mind what has been said above, it has been noted that by breathing in through either our left or right nostrils (but not both simultaneously), we can shift the level of activity between our left and right brain hemispheres (see *Rossi, 1986*). This can influence our behaviour and subjective experiences, simply because we are using the different regions of our brain. Interestingly, when we fall asleep, a sophisticated reflex

Nasal breathing as a means of changing your internal state of mind!

system is activated by pressure on our underarm as we lie on our side, which keeps the nostril on the upper side open.

As you read these very pages you can ascertain for yourself which of your nostrils are clear by simply pinching one of your nostrils and observing if you can breathe through the other nostril with relative ease or not, and then repeating the procedure with the other nostril. You will probably notice a greater degree of resistance or congestion in one nostril than the other, depending upon which brain hemisphere is being used to a greater extent. Now, try the method outlined below.

METHOD

1. Assess your present situation and feelings and gauge them on a scale of 0 (minimum) to 10 (maximum). For example, are you feeling a little down, angry and/or depressed?

2. Establish which of your nostrils is more congested by pinching one of the nostrils close as explained in the introduction above.

3. Now, lie down on your side with your *clear or less congested nostril* downwards. As a consequence, the clear nostril will become more congested, and the previously congested nostril more clear and less

congested. Hence, you will be gradually shifting your hemispheric activity from one side to the other, with implications in the personal way you deal with a particular situation.

4. Allow this process to continue for about 20 minutes, as you begin to relax even further, and just enjoy the experience. Allow whatever thoughts, feelings and insights to enter your awareness.

5. When you *feel* ready, allow yourself to reorientate to full wakeful alertness, knowing that a certain *healing* process has taken place within yourself. Stretch your arms and legs and take a deep breath.

6. Assess your present feelings, as in (1) above, and feel what a difference it has made compared to your initial assessment.

NOTES

- Be flexible with this technique and use it for the various different situations. The results you obtain will be unique to yourself. Remember, the main objective is to establish a holistic mental approach to the problematic issue by utilizing both right and left brain hemispheres.

- Don't attempt this method if you are suffering from a nasal cold, etc., as it will serve to only make you feel even more uncomfortable and uneasy.

A PERSONAL PHILOSOPHICAL REFLECTION

'We as human beings are in a perpetual state of flux as is everything around us in our universe. We can learn to accept, adapt and even modify these great forces that are at work, and to look upon it as a challenge and a constructive facilitator for change within our being, rather than an obstacle and a foe. To harness these forces to our advantage, we should strive towards self-development and collective progress – a humble wish worth striving for. Past lessons from history have taught us that those of us who arrogantly confront, defy, and show disrespect to these great forces of nature have always succumbed and have been engulfed by its vastness – like a drop in the ocean! We owe it to ourselves, and those around us, to take heed of the signs, and to follow the most appropriate path in our journey to a state of higher consciousness.'

A personal philosophical reflection.

APPENDIX

ORGANISATIONS AND SUPPORT GROUPS

Helpful information and support can be obtained from the following organisations:

British Association for Counselling and Psychotherapy
1 Regent Place
Rugby CV21 2PJ
Tel: 0870 4435252
Website: http://www.bacp.co.uk
E-mail: bacp@bacp.co.uk

British Association of Psychotherapists
37 Mapesbury Road
London NW2 4HJ
Tel: 020 8452 9823
Website: http://www.bap-psychtherapy.org
E-mail: mail@bap-psychotherapy.org

British Hypnotherapy Association
67 Upper Berkeley Street
London W1W 5PF
Tel: 020 7723 4443

Careline
Cardinal Heenan Centre
326–328 High Road
Ilford IG1 1QP
Tel: 020 8514 5444
Helpline: 020 8514 1177
Website: www.freezone.co.uk/t17survivors/page10.html
E-mail: careline@totalise.co.uk

First Steps to Freedom
7 Avon Court
School Lane
Kenilworth CV8 2GX
Tel: 01926 864473
Helpline: 01926 851608
Website: http://www.firststeps.demon.co.uk
E-mail: firststepstofreedom@compuserve.com

International Institute for NLP Psychotherapy
Marlin House
2 Coppice Close
The Street
Takeley
Nr. Bishop's Stortford CM22 6QB
Tel: 01279 873494
Website: http://www.nlp-psychotherapy.co.uk
E-mail: infoweb@marlin-nlp.co.uk

London College of Clinical Hypnosis
15 Connaught Square
London W2 2HG
Tel: 020 7402 9037
Website: http://www.lcch.co.uk
E-mail: lcch@lcch.co.uk

Mind (The Mental Health Charity)
Granta House
15–19 Broadway
London E15 4BQ
Tel: 020 8519 2122
Website: http://www.mind.org.uk
E-mail: contact@mind.org.uk

National Phobics Society
Zion Community Resource Centre
339 Stretford Road
Hulme
Manchester M15 4ZY
Tel: 0161 227 9898
Website: http://www.phobics-society.org.uk
E-mail: natphob.soc@good.co.uk

National Register of Hypnotherapists and Psychotherapists
12 Cross Street
Nelson BB9 7EN

Tel: 01282 716839
Helpline: 0800 161 3823
Website: http://www.nrhp.co.uk
E-mail: nrhp@btconnect.com

Seasonal Affective Disorder Association
PO Box 989
Steyning BN44 3HG
Tel: 01903 814942
Website: http://www.sada.org.uk/

Social Phobia and Anxiety
Kath Locke Centre
123 Moss Lane West
Hulme
Manchester M15 5DD
Tel: 0161 455 0215 or 0161 226 5412
or 0161 455 0211
Website: http://www.hometown.aol.com/SPAnxiety

UK Council for Psychotherapy
167–169 Great Portland Street
London W1W 5PF
Tel: 020 7436 3002
Website: http://www.psychotherapy.org.uk
E-mail: ukcp@psychotherapy.org.uk

GLOSSARY

Meanings and definitions provided are those which have been used within the context of the material discussed in this book.

Anxiety: A feeling of apprehension, uncertainty and fear, without an apparent stimulus, associated with physiological changes (e.g. a racing heart, increased perspiration, tremors, etc.).

Anxiolytics: These are various classes of anti-anxiety drugs prescribed to reduce anxiety.

Associated state (NLP): The experience of being in your body and experiencing all the related emotions.

Autosuggestion: To give a self-suggestion.

Benzodiazepines: A widely used group of drugs with a powerful action on the central nervous system which comprises of the brain and the spinal cord.

Circadian rhythm: A natural biological rhythm with an approximately 24-hour cycle, influencing blood pressure, body temperature, hormonal secretions, etc.

Conscious mind: The part of the mind that thinks, feels and acts in the present – a state of awareness.

Dissociated state (NLP): The experience of being outside your body and not experiencing the related emotions, e.g. as if you are watching yourself carry out a certain task within the mind's imagination.

Endorphins: Sometimes regarded as our natural feel-good chemicals produced by our brain. They are a group of endogenous polypeptide brain substances that bind to opiate receptor sites in various regions of the brain, thereby raising the pain threshold, and also giving an individual a feeling of well-being. They play an important role in emotional behaviour patterns.

Fear: A normal, emotional response (in contrast to anxiety and phobia) to a consciously recognised external source(s) of danger which is manifested by alarm, apprehension or disquiet.

Homeostasis: The maintenance of a balanced state by the initiation of some kind of regulatory mechanism.

Hypnosis: An altered state of awareness and concentration, in which it has been shown that there is an increased responsiveness to suggestions (see also the entry on trance).

Hypnotherapy: A directive form of psychotherapy using trance as a facilitator for internal change.

Hypnotics: This category includes a range of drugs for inducing sleep.

Mind: The totality of the conscious and unconscious mental processes.

Modelling: The process of imitating and performing an observed behaviour pattern.

Panic attack: An extreme and unreasoning fear and anxiety accompanied by various symptoms including breathlessness, sweating, sickness, dizziness, etc.

Phobia: Any persistent, intense, abnormal dread or fear, e.g. nyctophobia (fear of the night), etc.

Psychosomatic: The interaction between the mental (psychic) and bodily (somatic) dimensions to produce an effect, i.e. the symptom. It is a mind–body relationship.

Reframing: Redefining and reinterpreting an event or situation.

Stress: A physiological response and a negative emotional state produced by a stressor. It is, by one definition, the result of other pressures, e.g. psychological, social, etc.

Stress management: A range of psychological techniques used for reducing stress.

Stressor: The cause or source of stress.

Subconscious mind: See entry (below) on the unconscious mind.

Suggestibility: The tendency to react to suggestion(s).

Suggestion: The uncritical acceptance of an idea,

opinion, etc., by direct or indirect methods, and so guiding someone to think and/or behave in a certain manner.

Trance: A form of focused attention and an altered state of awareness (see also the entry on hypnosis).

Ultradian rhythm: A natural biological rhythm occurring about every 90–120 minutes.

Unconscious mind: Also referred to as the subconscious mind. It is the part of the mind that influences our thoughts and behaviour, outside of our normal conscious awareness.

BIBLIOGRAPHY

Achterberg, J. (1985) *Imagery and healing*. Boston: Shambala.

Aldrich, K. and Berstein, D. (1987) The effect of time of day on hypnotisability. *International Journal of Clinical and Experimental Hypnosis*, **35**: 141–5.

Alexander, F. (1950) *Psychosomatic medicine*. New York: W.W. Norton.

Bandler, R. and Grinder, J. (1981) *Trance-formations: Neuro-linguistic programming and the structure of hypnosis*. Utah : Real People Press.

Bandler, R. and Grinder, J. (1979) *Frogs into princes: The introduction to neuro-linguistic programming*. Guernsey: The Guernsey Press Co. Ltd.

Barber, T.X. (1984) Changing unchangeable bodily processes by (hypnotic) suggestions: A new look at hypnosis, cognitions, imagining, and the mind-body problem. *Advances*, **1**: 7–40.

Bloom, F., Lazerson, A. and Hofstadter, L. (1985) *Brain, mind and behavior*. New York: W.H.Freeman.

Blythe, P. (1976) *Self-hypnotism*. London: Arthur Barker.

Bowers, K. and Kelly, P. (1979) Stress, disease, psychotherapy and hypnosis. *Journal of Abnormal Psychology*, **88**: 490–505.

Brown, P. (1991) Ultradian rhythms of cerebral function and hypnosis. *Contemporary Hypnosis*, **8**: 17–24.

Erickson, M.H. and Rossi, E.L. (1981) *Hypnotherapy: An exploratory casebook*. New York: Irvington Publishers.

Erickson, M.H. and Rossi, E.L. (1981) *Experiencing hypnosis: Therapeutic approaches to altered states*. New York: Irvington Publishers.

Erickson, M.H. and Rossi, E.L. (1976) *Hypnotic realities*. New York: Irvington Publishers.

Gibson, H.B. and Heap, M. (1991) *Hypnosis in therapy*. Hove: Lawrence Erlbaum Associates.

Gross, R.D. (1992) *Psychology: The science of mind and behaviour* (2nd edn). London: Hodder and Stoughton.

Haley, J. (1973) *Uncommon therapy: The psychiatric techniques of Milton. H. Erickson*. California: Meta.

Haley, J. (1963) *Strategies of psychotherapy*. New York: Grune and Stratton.

Hammond, D.C. (1990) *Handbook of hypnotic suggestions and metaphors*. New York: W.W. Norton and Company.

Holroyd, K. and Lazarus, R. (1982) Stress, coping and somatic adaptation, in Goldberger, L. and Bresnitz, S. (eds) *Handbook of stress*. New York: Free Press.

Hopkins, S.J. (1992) *Principal drugs* (10th edn). London: Mosby Year Book Europe Ltd.

Knight, S. (1995) *NLP at work: The difference that makes a difference in business.* London: Nicholas Brealey Publishing.

Kroger, W.S. (1977) *Clinical and experimental hypnosis* (2nd edn). Philadelphia: J.B. Lippincott Company.

Lazarus, A.A. (1971) *Behaviour therapy and beyond.* New York: McGraw-Hill.

Lloyd, D. and Stupfel, M. (1991) The occurrence and functions of ultradian rhythms. *Biological Reviews,* **66**: 275–99.

Morgan, D. (1996) *The principles of hypnotherapy.* Bradford: Eildon Press.

Naish, P. (ed.) (1986) *What is hypnosis? Current theories and research.* Philadelphia: Open University Press.

O'Connor, J. and Seymour, J. (1990) *Introducing neuro-linguistic programming: Psychological skills for understanding and influencing people.* London: The Aquarian Press.

Reber, A.S. (1995) *Dictionary of psychology* (2nd edn). London: Penguin Books Ltd.

Rossi, E.L. (1986) *The psychobiology of mind-body healing: New concepts of therapeutic hypnosis.* New York: W.W. Norton and Company.

Rossi, E.L. (1982) Hypnosis and ultradian cycles: A new states theory of hypnosis?. *American Journal of Clinical Hypnosis,* **25**: 21–32.

Rossi, E.L. (1980) *The collected papers of Milton Erickson on hypnosis (Vols 1–4)*. New York: Irvington Press.

Rossi, E.L. and Ryan, M.O. (eds) (1998) *The seminars, workshops and lectures of Milton. H. Erickson (Vols 1–4)*. London: Free Association Books.

Rowshan, A. (1993) *Stress: An owner's manual*. Oxford: Oneworld Publications.

Sperling, A. and Martin, K. (1982) *Psychology*. Oxford: Butterworth–Heinemann Ltd.

Spiegel, H. and Spiegel, D. (1978) *Trance and treatment*. New York: Basic Books.

Waxman, D. (1989) *Hartland's medical and dental hypnosis* (3rd edn). London: Baillière Tindal.

Wickramasekera, I. (ed.)(1976) *Biofeedback, behaviour therapy and hypnosis*. Chicago, IL: Nelson–Hall.

Wolpe, J. (1973) *The practice of behaviour therapy* (2nd edn.). New York: Pergamon Press.

Wright, M.E. and Wright, B.A. (1987) *Clinical practice of hypnotherapy*. New York: The Guilford Press.

Yapko, M.D. (1994) *When living hurts: Directives for treating depressions*. New York: Brunner/ Mazel.

Yapko, M.D. (1992) *Hypnosis and the treatment of depressions: Strategies for change*. New York: Brunner/Mazel.

Yapko, M.D. (1990) *Trancework: An introduction to the practice of clinical hypnosis* (2nd edn). New York: Brunner/Mazel.

Yapko, M.D. (ed.) (1989) *Brief therapy approaches to treating anxiety and depressions.* New York: Brunner/Mazel.

Yapko, M.D. (1986) *Hypnotic and strategic interventions: Principles and practice.* New York: Irvington Publishers.

Young, L.Y., Koda-Kimble, M.A., Guglielmo, B. J. and Kradjan, W.A. (1989) *Handbook of applied therapeutics.* Vancouver, WA: Applied Therapeutics Inc.

Zeig, J. (ed.) (1984) *Ericksonian approaches to hypnosis and psychotherapy.* New York: Brunner/Mazel.

Zeig, J. (1980) Symptom prescription and Ericksonian principles of hypnosis and psychotherapy. *American Journal of Clinical Hypnosis,* **23**: 16–22.

INDEX